Published by:
A Book's Mind
PO Box 272847
Fort Collins, CO 80527

Copyright © 2018 Sue Mateer
ISBN: 978-1-944255-80-0
Printed in the United States of America

CASSIDY'S PRESENT

BE HERE NOW

SUE MATEER

ILLUSTRATED BY TENNY OSTREM

RESOURCE GUIDE BY APRIL STUTTERS

Cassidy walks Anna and Charlie to school each day.
Today, Charlie says, "Look at the snow! The last time it snowed this much,
I lost my boot. My foot was so cold when I got home."

He is very worried about past experiences in the snow.

Anna says, "What will happen if it keeps snowing and doesn't stop?
Will we get stuck at school?" She is nervous about what might happen next.

"Be careful Cassidy, don't get lost in the snow," says Charlie.

What is Cassidy doing in the snow?

Have you ever caught a snowflake on your tongue or made a snowman?

Now it is spring. Cassidy notices colorful flowers and sweet smells.

Anna is troubled, "What if we have a surprise quiz on Friday and I don't have time to finish the quiz?"

Charlie is concerned about what happened last year in the spring. He says, "Next week is spring break. Last year I got very sick and had to stay in bed for three days."

Anna wonders, "What is Cassidy getting into now?"

What does Cassidy smell?

What colors does she see?

Have you ever picked a flower?
What does it smell or feel like?

It is summer—hot and sunny. Cassidy walks with the children
to swim class and wishes she could jump in the pool.

Charlie, again thinking back, says, "Last year at swim class I got sunburned.
Once I forgot my goggles so I had to sit out. I didn't like swim class last year."

Anna is again anxious about what might happen in the future.
She frets, "When we finish swim class, we will have to take a final test.
I will have to hold my breath underwater. Oh no!"

Charlie forgets his worries for a moment and
wonders what Cassidy will do while they swim.
"Anna, maybe someday we could go swimming with Cassidy!"

What is Cassidy doing?
Have you ever felt the warm
sun on your skin or felt a butterfly
kiss on your nose?

What does water feel like when
you go swimming?

Summer is over, it is autumn and Cassidy is again walking the children to school.
Anna, still somewhat concerned about what may happen next says,
"I wonder who my new teacher will be. What if none of my friends are in my class?"

Charlie is sporting a new backpack. He chooses to focus on a past mishap and says,
"I hope this new backpack doesn't rip.
Last year my backpack ripped and my books landed in a puddle."

Anna hears the geese overhead and watches Cassidy frolic in the leaves. For a moment
she puts aside her concern for the future and imagines the fun she could have right now.
"Charlie, wouldn't it be fun to jump in a big pile of leaves with Cassidy?"

What does Cassidy see?
Have you ever watched
leaves fall from a tree?

What sounds do you hear in the fall?
Have you ever drawn a picture of a leaf?

It is now snowy outside and almost time for winter break.

Cassidy is waiting outside the school for Charlie and Anna.

Charlie thinks, "I'm going to stop worrying about what happened
yesterday or long ago. I can learn from the past but I want to live in the present.

Today I will play with Cassidy and tickle her tummy!"

Anna is watching Cassidy play outside.
She thinks, "Why worry about what might or might not happen
tomorrow or next year? I can plan for the future but I want to live in the present.
Today I will play with Cassidy and scratch her behind her ears!"

Anna and Charlie have learned from Cassidy to appreciate the present moment
and everything it has to offer. Cassidy is a very happy dog!

Resource Guide
By April Stutters
Why This Book Is Important

Learning how to soothe themselves is perhaps the most important skill children can learn. Whether we find calm by petting a dog, listening to music, or taking a few deep breaths, we can all find our way into relaxation and self-regulation. Finding our unique personal combination of ways to soothe ourselves is key to weathering the many ups and downs of life. It is wise to have a repertoire of calming techniques because one technique might not be available - it may not be possible to listen to music when we are stressed! Many of us don't address a child's stress or anxiety until it is a problem. However, we can help relieve stress and achieve a better quality of life more successfully if we build mindfulness and stress management into our daily lives.

Leading by example is one of the best ways to foster a positive approach to handling stress and to teach the skills to address it. Whether we work with children in any of a variety of situations or just with our own child, we find that if a child experiences a lot of anxiety or has a panic attack, the most important and helpful tool we have is ourselves. If we get agitated, it will increase the child's agitation. Likewise, our unruffled demeanor may lower a child's stress level. Staying calm is an intervention in itself.

This resource guide covers exercises, materials which can be kept on hand, programs that children can explore either with an adult or by themselves, and more. When professional assistance is needed, this guide it can help to find it. The guide is not meant to be all-encompassing, but the majority of these ideas, suggestions, and activities are research-based, and are used in therapeutic work with children. It is our hope that they will provide some relief and give you and the child new techniques and skills to reduce stress and improve your lives. Although the resource guide is directed primarily to parents and primary caregivers, anyone who works with children may find it valuable for the children around them - and for themselves as well.

Exercises

First, a hint for getting started. Begin where your child is right now, whether the child is calm or highly agitated. Refrain from judging yourself for either your child's stress or your own.

Guided Imagery for Meditation

Our imaginations are powerful. In many ways, worry is rooted in the imagination. If imagination plays a part in getting us agitated, imagination can also help us to relax.

Here we will mention a few of many written resources which may prove helpful. The book *Ready... Set... R.E.L.A.X.: A Research-Based Program of Relation, Learning, and Self Esteem for Children,* by Jeffrey S. Allen and Roger J. Klein, has been used successfully in homes and classrooms across the country. It offers tools for overcoming anxiety that include music, muscle relaxation, and storytelling. Additionally, author Maureen Garth has written many enchanting books of meditations for children, including *Starbright, Moonbeam,* and *Earthlight.*

Don't forget to draw on your own resources. You can make up your own stories using guiding images which come from things you know the child likes and appreciates.

Breathing Exercises

Teaching your child to breathe deeply into his or her belly, hold the breath, and then release it slowly is a useful stress-reduction technique. Breathing deeply into our diaphragms instead of taking shorter breaths into our lungs can lower our heart rates to bring our bodies into a relaxed state. Doing so moves us from the fight, flight, and freeze divisions of our nervous system to the division that is often referred to as "rest and digest." When we were babies, we breathed this way naturally. But as we grow older, if we're not mindful, we tend to take shallower breaths into our lungs only—and that can stress our systems.

An easy way to teach a child this skill is to have the child lie on his or her back. Place something - like a shoe, a book, or stuffed animal on the child's tummy. Both feeling the slight weight of the object and seeing the object rise and fall are helpful in this exercise. When the child breathes in, he or she focuses on bringing air into the belly and making the object go up. Tell the child to use core muscles to push the air in the belly out. Once the child is able to do this exercise, have him or her do it for five minutes. The longer the child can breathe out in and out, the deeper the relaxation.

Guided Muscle Relaxation

This quick and simple exercise can be done anywhere. Ask the child to squeeze his or her hands really tightly, as if squeezing juice from an orange. Then ask your child to slowly release the muscles. Repeat this exercise three times.

An extension of this technique can help your child relax before sleep. Guide your child to tense and relax muscles throughout the body, starting with the feet. You can guide your child by saying, "Tighten the muscles in your toes and squeeze, squeeze, squeeze. Now release. Tighten the muscles in your ankles, tight, tight, tight. Now release." Have the child tighten and release muscles all the way up to and including his or her face. For the final step, have the child tighten the whole body and release.

Five Things Exercise

Using all five of our senses can bring us into a relaxed state. This exercise is used in schools and hospitals to help bring a person into the present moment. Because answers to the last two questions can be harder to find depending on where a person is, we often focus on just the first two to three sensory questions below so the child can be successful. You can try it right now with yourself.

Tell me five things you see in this room/place.

Tell me five things that you feel by touch (such as clothes against the skin).

Tell me five things you hear.

Tell me five things that you smell.

Tell me five things you taste.

Continue the narrative, reducing the numbers. *Now, tell me four things you see, you feel, you hear, you smell, you taste. Now, three things... then two, then one. What do you notice about yourself now?*

Chocolate Kiss Exercise

This exercise teaches mindfulness. Take your time with the exercise and try to make it last at least three minutes so the child will grasp the point. Have the child close his or her eyes and place a wrapped chocolate in his or her hand. The following questions and suggestions can help guide the exercise:

Tell me about the sound of the wrapper. How heavy is the chocolate kiss? How does it feel in your hands? Can you smell it? What does it remind you of? How are you feeling right now? Unwrap it very slowly. What does the texture feel like on your hands? Place it on your tongue but don't chew. Is there one part of your mouth where you can taste it more than another part? Tell me how it feels in your mouth. What are your teeth doing? Roll it around in your mouth. Does the taste change? Now go ahead and finish eating it. Do you feel different? Discuss the whole experience with the child when finished. This exercise can be adapted to work with a raisin as well.

Taking a Family Day Off

Families and individuals who are trying to step outside of our stressful world are creating their own break from technology and other experiences that impede mindfulness. Your family could decide to take one day off a month. Design your own Family Day Off by asking family members these questions. *What things that we do together bring us close to each other?* See what the answers are. Make a list. Don't prompt unless the silence lasts longer than a minute (watch your watch – a minute of silence is a long time). Then ask; *What things keep us further apart?* List those answers as well. Use both lists to plan the day. Many people start with a non-technology day and just have fun together. You might want to visit the following website for ideas and resources: nationaldayofunplugging.com.

Yoga

Yoga is a great way for kids to learn about relaxation and self-care in a fun and playful way. Yoga increases strength, flexibility, focus, and balance. It teaches breathing exercises and it teaches us how to listen to our bodies. Many yoga studios have classes for children and many video classes are available.

Mindfulness Curriculum

The Hawn Foundation, the brainchild of actress and comedienne Goldie Hawn, has worked with neuroscientists to create programs for schools that focus on mindfulness, especially to reduce stress. The curriculum is called Mind-Up. The exercises can be done at home or at school. You can get to know this curriculum at *mindup.org*.

Apps

Apps offer an amazing opportunity to present children with information through a channel they already enjoy using. New apps to help children manage stress are constantly becoming available, but here are a few of the tried and true to start you on the journey.

Younger Children	*Older Children and Adults*
Breathe, Think, Do (Sesame Street)	Headspace: Guided Meditation and Mindfulness (Headspace Inc.)
Wince—Don't Feed the WorryBug (iMagine Machine)	Brainwave (Banzai Labs)
Sleep Meditations for Kids (Christiane Kerr)	Breathe2Relax (National Center for Telehealth and Technology)
Kids Meditation App—My Light Shines Bright (The Chopra Center)	Insight Timer—Meditation App (Insight Network Inc)

Professional Assistance

Biofeedback

Biofeedback offers a concrete and measurable way to demonstrate and teach techniques of relaxation. Individual are connected to painless electrical sensors that help them to receive information (feedback) about their bodies (bio). The instruments used give precise, immediate, and meaningful auditory and/or visual feedback about the user's physiology. For example, a child watching a monitor uses his or her breath to relax the body and get the hot air balloon shown on the monitor off the ground. Working with a professional who has state-of-the-art equipment ensures that the biofeedback will be successful and it may be covered under your health insurance.

You can also bring biofeedback into your home through a program called *Inner Balance*, by HeartMath. It works on a phone or tablet. Although the app is free, you will need to purchase the sensor from *heartmath.com*.

Therapy

Although every child can benefit from mindfulness activities, some children may need a little extra help. To choose the right therapist, start by finding out which child and adolescent therapists in your area are covered by your insurance. You can find a biography and a photograph of most therapists at *therapists.psychologytoday.com*. Once you have chosen two or three potential therapists, ask for a no-cost, informational consultation. A therapist should be willing to answer any questions you may have about training, methods, and fees.

After you talk to a therapist about his or her background and training, consider asking the following as well as any additional questions you have:

- *What is your basic approach to therapy? What do you think is its most important element?*
- *Have you worked with children who have similar challenges to those my child faces?*
- *Will you include family members in the therapy?*
- *How will I know that my child is getting better?*
- *How will you and I communicate with each other?*
- *Would you be interested in working with my child's school?*
- *Are you willing to coordinate my child's treatment with our pediatrician?*
- *Will you share a success story with me?*

If you and your child both feel a strong positive connection with a therapist, the therapy is more likely to be a positive and rewarding experience. Multiple studies indicate that a good fit between the therapist and the client is the most important element in counseling, so it is important to take your time and make the best choice.

In Closing

Based on research, the following activities can successfully reduce stress:

- Laughter
- Animals
- Play
- Family meals
- Physical exercise
- Music
- Meditation
- Aroma therapy
- Martial arts
- And more...

We hope you find the resources listed above helpful and that they bring relaxation, rejuvenation, and joy into your and your child's life.

With warm regards,

April, Tenny, and Sue

CPSIA information can be obtained
at www.ICGtesting.com
Printed in the USA
LVHW071646240122
709246LV00009B/360